Success
Assessment Papers

More Non-Verbal Reasoning

age 10 – 11

Peter Francis

Sample page

paper number for
quick reference

PAPER 1

example at the
beginning of each
section

Example

Work out how the pair of images on the top line go together.
Then find the image on the next line that completes the
second pair in the same way as the first pair. Circle the letter
under the image that you think is the correct answer.

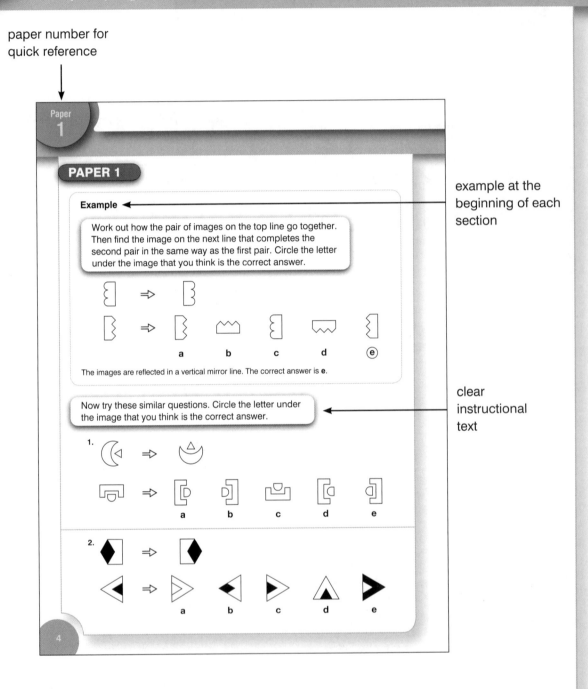

The images are reflected in a vertical mirror line. The correct answer is **e**.

clear
instructional
text

Now try these similar questions. Circle the letter under
the image that you think is the correct answer.

1.

a   b   c   d   e

2.

a   b   c   d   e

4

Contents

PAPER 1

Example

Work out how the pair of images on the top line go together. Then find the image on the next line that completes the second pair in the same way as the first pair. Circle the letter under the image that you think is the correct answer.

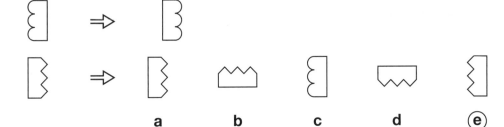

The images are reflected in a vertical mirror line. The correct answer is **e**.

Now try these similar questions. Circle the letter under the image that you think is the correct answer.

1.

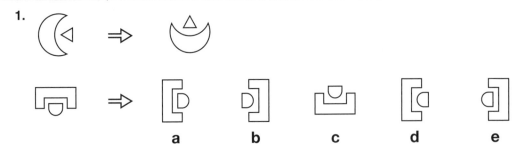

2.

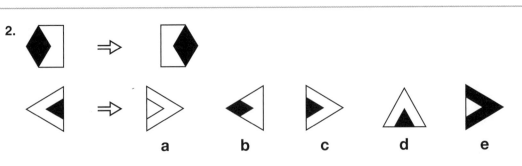

3.

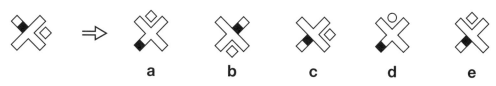

          a   **b**   **c**   **d**   **e**

4.  as

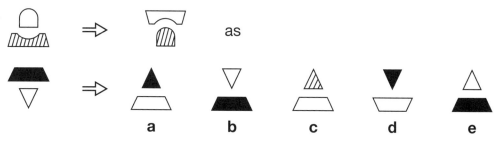

          a   **b**   **c**   **d**   **e**

5.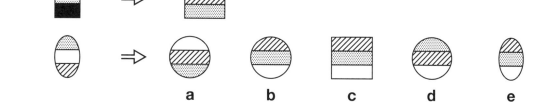

          a   **b**   **c**   **d**   **e**

6.

          a   **b**   **c**   **d**   **e**

7.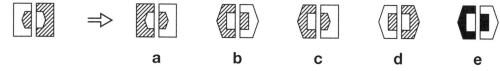

          a   **b**   **c**   **d**   **e**

8.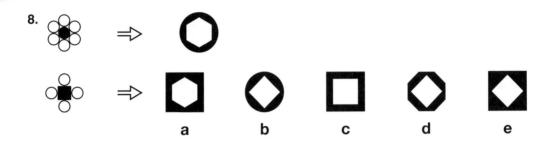

a   b   c   d   e

/8

Example

One of the boxes on the second line completes the sequence or pattern on the top line. Circle the letter under the box that you think is the correct answer.

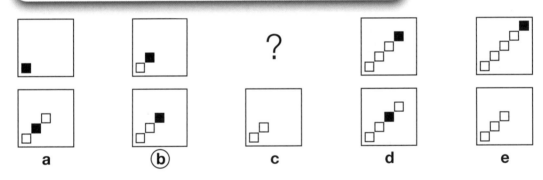

a   (b)   c   d   e

Looking at the boxes from left to right, the number of squares increases by one each time. The new square, added at the end of the pattern, is shaded black; the previous square becomes white. The correct answer is **b**.

Now try these similar questions. Circle the letter under the box that you think is the correct answer.

9.

a   b   c   d   e

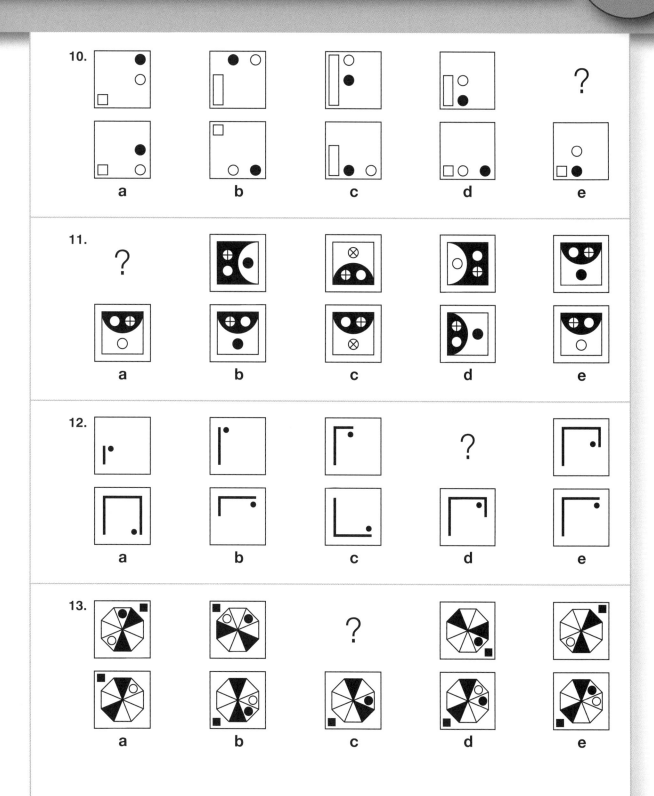

14.

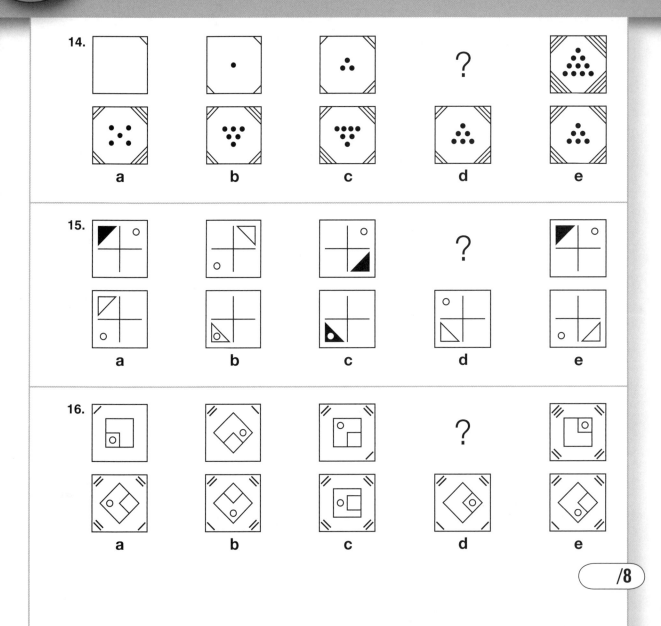

a   b   c   d   e

15.

a   b   c   d   e

16.

a   b   c   d   e

/8

Example

One of the boxes is missing from the grid on the left. Work out which of the five boxes on the right completes the grid. Circle the letter under the box that you think is the correct answer.

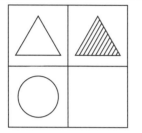

a   b   ©c   d   e

As the images in the boxes move across from left to right, they become shaded with diagonal stripes. The correct answer is **c**.

Now try these similar questions. Circle the letter under the box that you think is the correct answer.

17.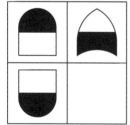

a   b   c   d   e

18.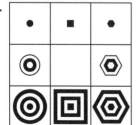

a   b   c   d   e

19.

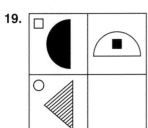

a   b   c   d   e

20.

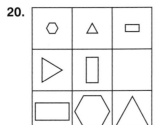

a   b   c   d   e

21.

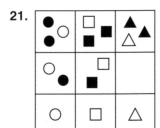

a   b   c   d   e

22.

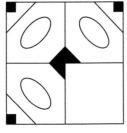

a   b   c   d   e

23.

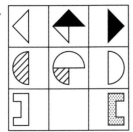

a   b   c   d   e

24.

                         a   b   c   d   e

/8

Example

Work out what makes the two images on the left similar to each other. Then find the image on the right that is *most like* the two images on the left. Circle the letter under the image that you think is the correct answer.

  |

                         a   (b)   c   d   e

The two images on the left are right-angled triangles with two sides of equal length. Shape **b** is the only other right-angled triangle that has two sides of equal length.

Now try these similar questions. Circle the letter under the image that you think is the correct answer.

25.

  |

                         a   b   c   d   e

26.

a   b   c   d   e

27.

a   b   c   d   e

28.

a   b   c   d   e

29.

a   b   c   d   e

30.

a   b   c   d   e

31.

a   b   c   d   e

32.

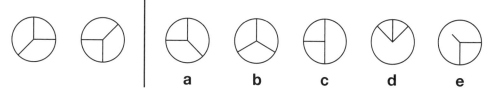

a   b   c   d   e

/8

Example

The four images on the top line each have a code. Work out how the codes go with these images, then find the missing code for the image on the next line. Circle the letter under the code that you think is the correct answer.

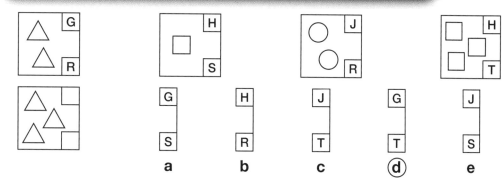

The image with the missing code has three triangles. Triangles have the letter code G. Three has the letter code T. The correct answer is **d**.

Now try these similar questions. Circle the letter under the code that you think is the correct answer.

33.

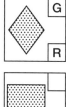

a   b   c   d   e

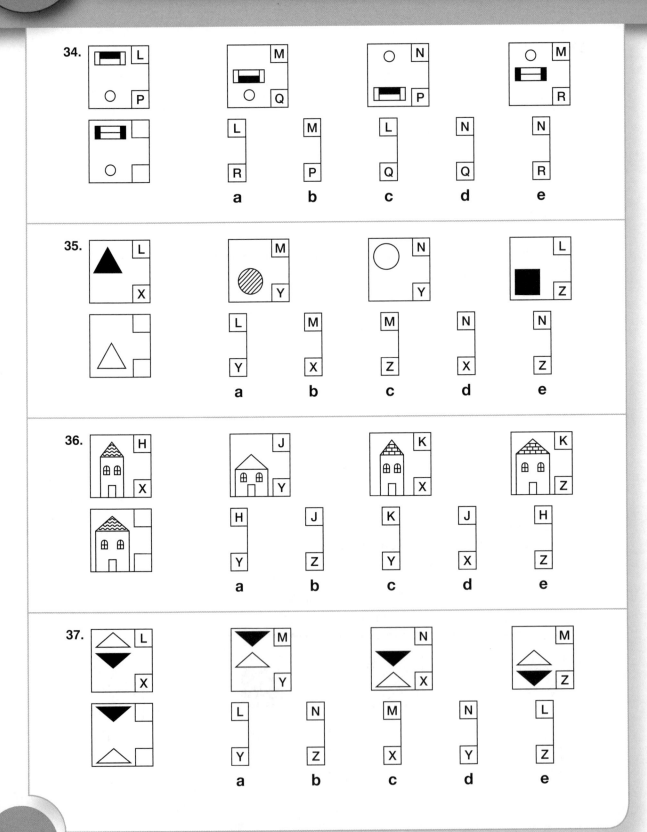

34.

35.

36.

37.

38.

Q G L	R H M	S G N	T J M

a
Q
H
N

b
R
G
M

c
T
H
L

d
S
H
M

e
T
J
L

39.

R X	S Y	T Z	R Y

a
T
Y

b
S
X

c
R
Z

d
S
Z

e
T
X

40.

R X J	S Y K	S Z J	T Y L

a
R
Y
K

b
T
Z
K

c
R
Z
L

d
T
Y
J

e
S
X
L

/8

/40

PAPER 2

Example

Look at the line of five images. Work out what connects *four* of the images and makes the other image the odd one out. Circle the letter under the image most *unlike* the others.

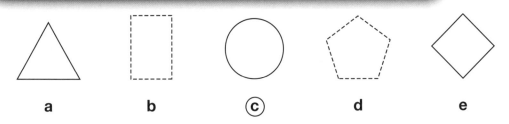

| a | b | c | d | e |

Shapes a, b, d and e all have straight sides; shape c is the only curved shape. The shape most unlike the others is **c**.

Now try these similar questions. Circle the letter under the image that you think is the correct answer.

1.

| a | b | c | d | e |

2.

| a | b | c | d | e |

3.

| a | b | c | d | e |

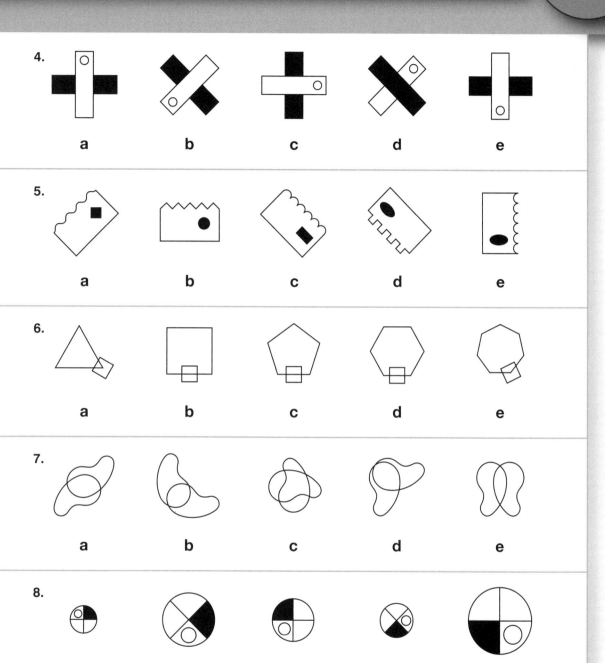

4.
    a   b   c   d   e

5.
    a   b   c   d   e

6.
    a   b   c   d   e

7.
    a   b   c   d   e

8.
    a   b   c   d   e

/8

Example

The four images on the top line each have a code. Work out how the codes go with these images, then find the missing code for the image on the next line. Circle the letter under the code that you think is the correct answer.

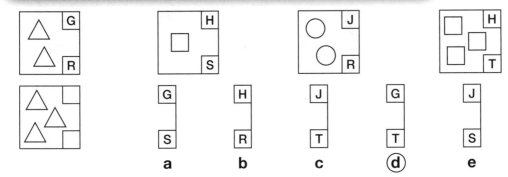

The image with the missing code has three triangles. Triangles have the letter code G. Three has the letter code T. The correct answer is **d**.

Now try these similar questions. Circle the letter under the code that you think is the correct answer.

9.

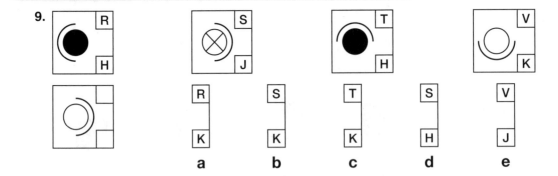

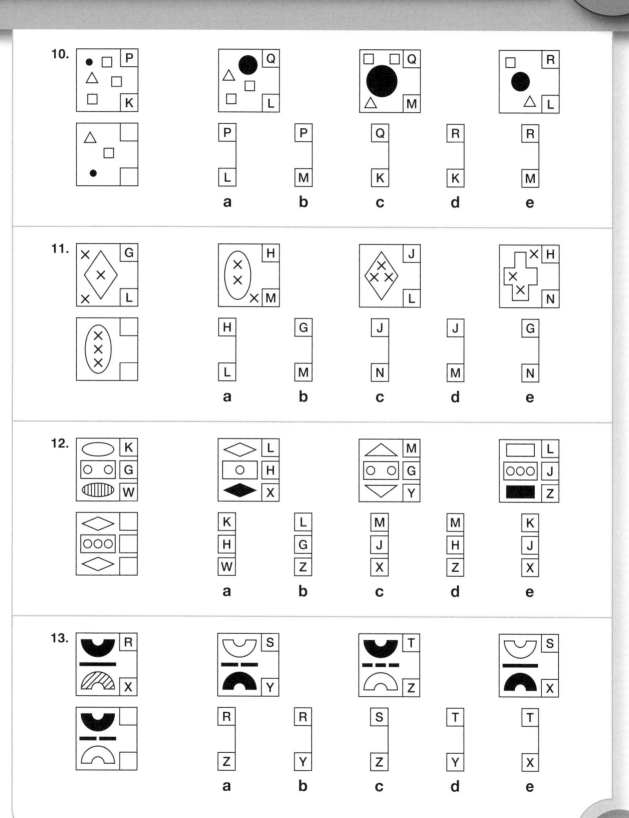

14.

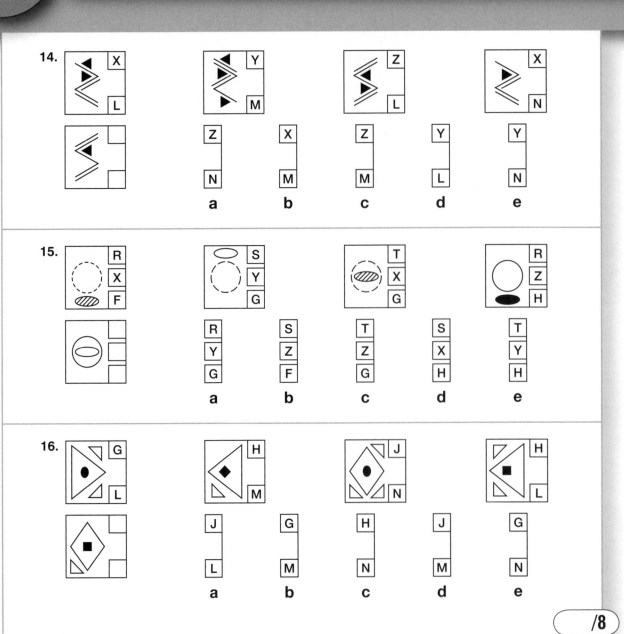

15.

16.

a　　　b　　　c　　　d　　　e

/8

Example

One of the boxes is missing from the grid on the left. Work out which of the five boxes on the right completes the grid. Circle the letter under the box that you think is the correct answer.

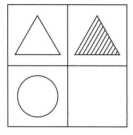

a   b   ⓒ   d   e

As the images in the boxes move across from left to right, they become shaded with diagonal stripes. The correct answer is **c**.

Now try these similar questions. Circle the letter under the box that you think is the correct answer.

17.

a   b   c   d   e

18.

a   b   c   d   e

19.

20.

21.

22.

23.

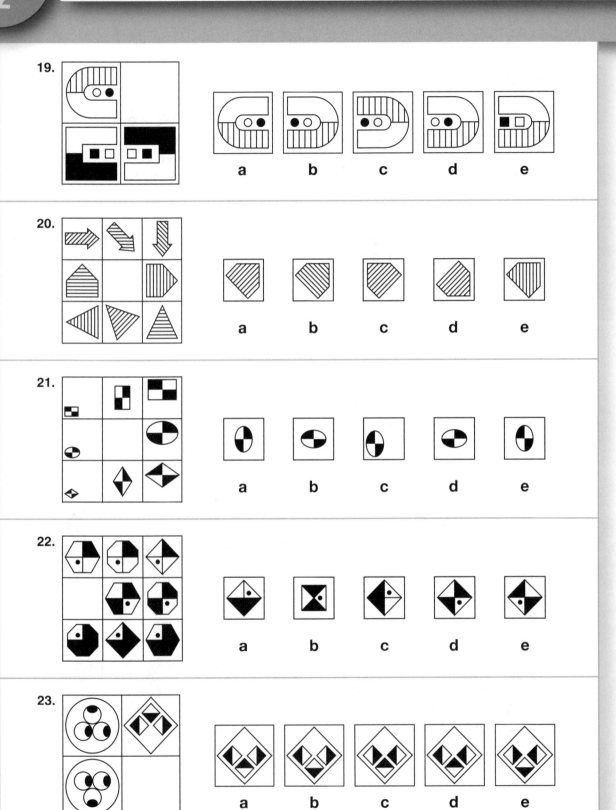

a   b   c   d   e

24.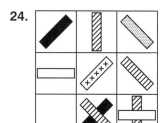

a   b   c   d   e

/8

Example

Work out how the pair of images on the top line go together. Then find the image on the next line that completes the second pair in the same way as the first pair. Circle the letter under the image that you think is the correct answer.

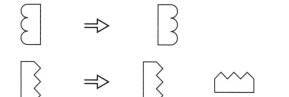

a   b   c   d   e

The images are reflected in a vertical mirror line. The correct answer is **e**.

Now try these similar questions. Circle the letter under the image that you think is the correct answer.

25.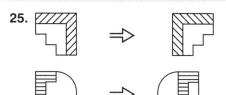

a   b   c   d   e

26.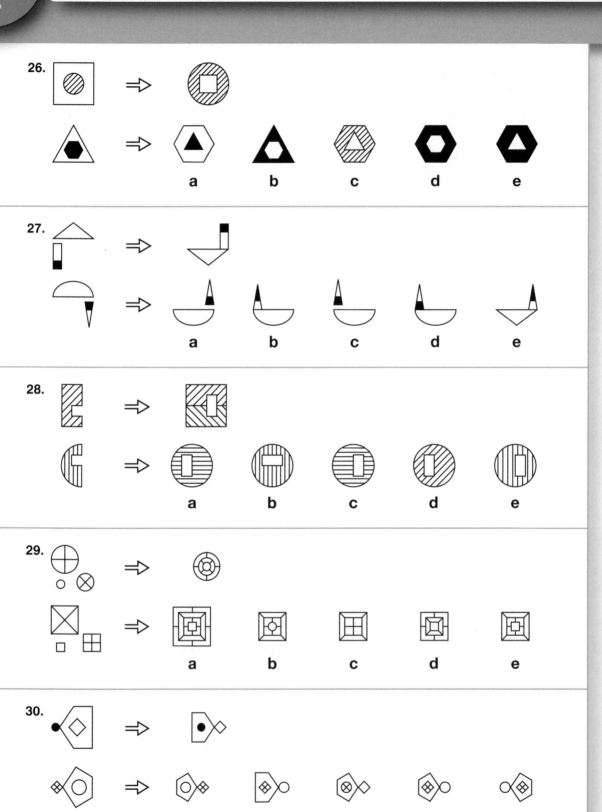

27.

28.

29.

30.

31.

a   b   c   d   e

32.

a   b   c   d   e

/8

Example

One of the boxes on the second line completes the sequence or pattern on the top line. Circle the letter under the box that you think is the correct answer.

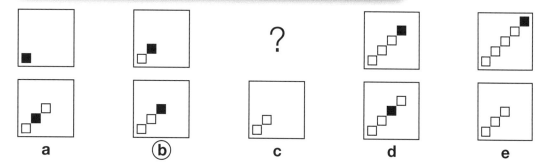

a   (b)   c   d   e

Looking at the boxes from left to right, the number of squares increases by one each time. The new square, added at the end of the pattern, is shaded black; the previous square becomes white. The correct answer is **b**.

Now try these similar questions. Circle the letter under the box that you think is the correct answer.

33.

   ?

a   b   c   d   e

34.

    ?

a   b   c   d   e

35.

   ?

a   b   c   d   e

36.

?

a   b   c   d   e

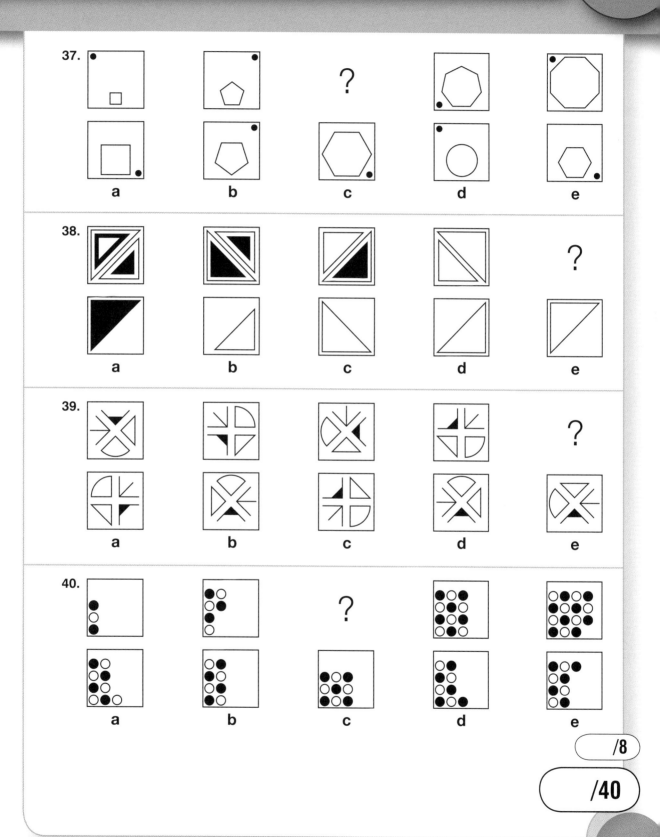

37.

a   b   c   d   e

38.

a   b   c   d   e

39.

a   b   c   d   e

40.

a   b   c   d   e

/8

/40

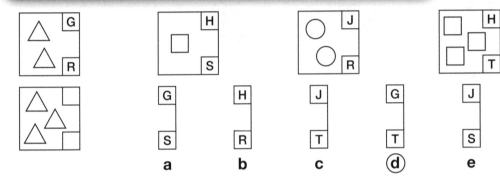

PAPER 3

Example

The four images on the top line each have a code. Work out how the codes go with these images, then find the missing code for the image on the next line. Circle the letter under the code that you think is the correct answer.

a   b   c   ⓓ   e

The image with the missing code has three triangles. Triangles have the letter code G. Three has the letter code T. The correct answer is **d**.

Now try these similar questions. Circle the letter under the code that you think is the correct answer.

1.

a   b   c   d   e

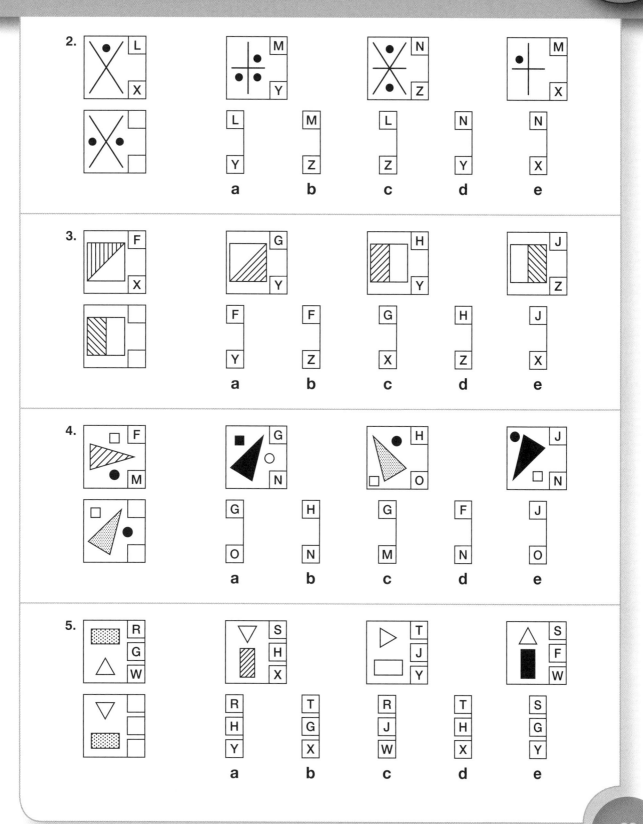

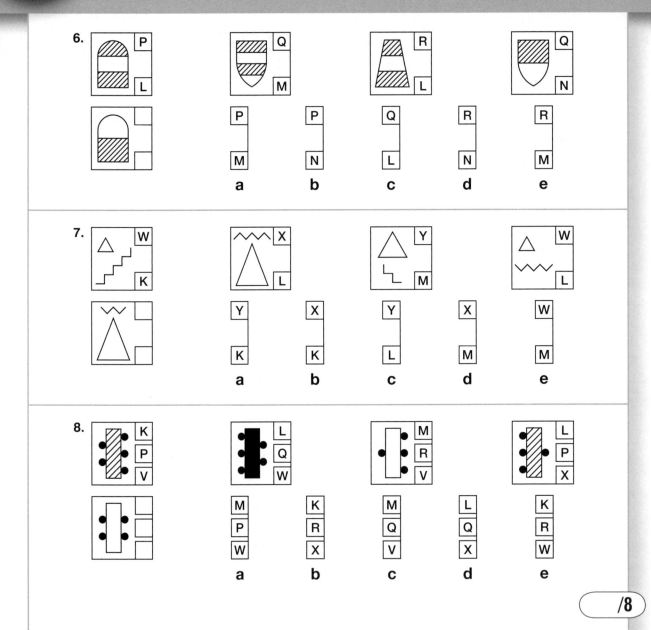

6.

a   b   c   d   e

7.

a   b   c   d   e

8.

a   b   c   d   e

/8

Example

Work out how the pair of images on the top line go together. Then find the image on the next line that completes the second pair in the same way as the first pair. Circle the letter under the image that you think is the correct answer.

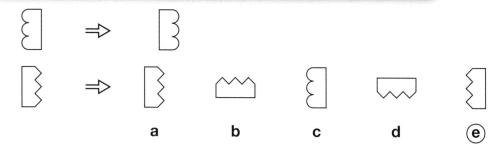

The images are reflected in a vertical mirror line. The correct answer is **e**.

Now try these similar questions. Circle the letter under the image that you think is the correct answer.

9.

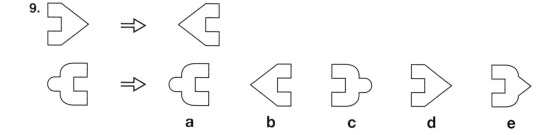

10.

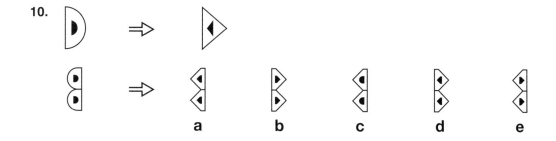

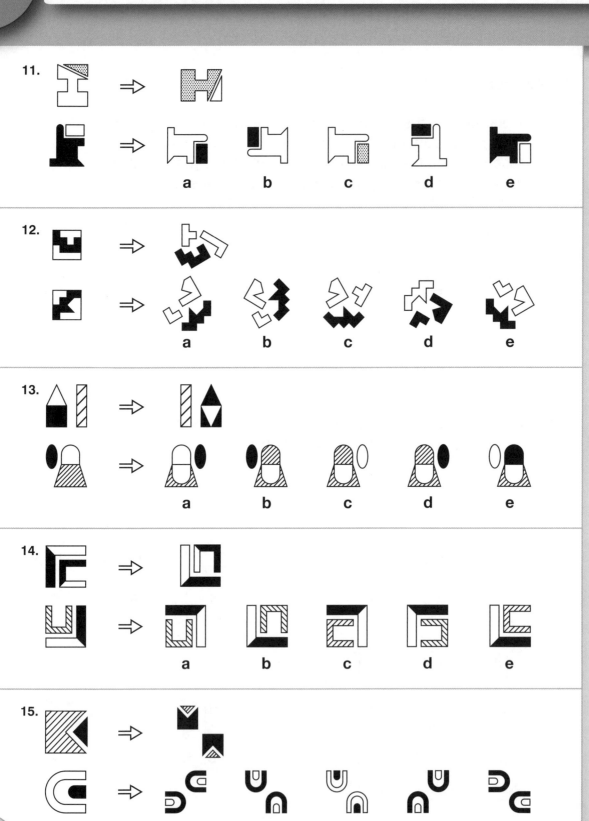

16.

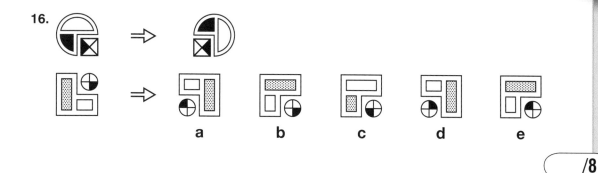

a   b   c   d   e

/8

Example

One of the boxes is missing from the grid on the left. Work out which of the five boxes on the right completes the grid. Circle the letter under the box that you think is the correct answer.

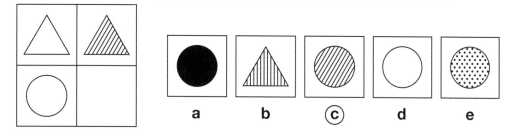

As the images in the boxes move across from left to right, they become shaded with diagonal stripes. The correct answer is **c**.

Now try these similar questions. Circle the letter under the box that you think is the correct answer.

17.

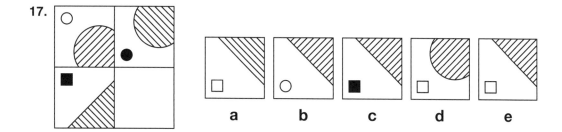

a   b   c   d   e

18.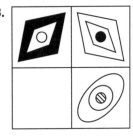

a   b   c   d   e

19.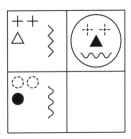

a   b   c   d   e

20.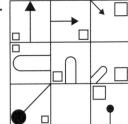

a   b   c   d   e

21.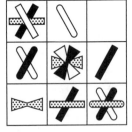

a   b   c   d   e

22.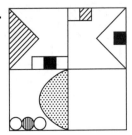

a   b   c   d   e

23.

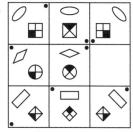

a b c d e

24.

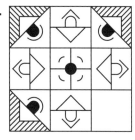

a b c d e

/8

Example

> One of the boxes on the second line completes the sequence or pattern on the top line. Circle the letter under the box that you think is the correct answer.

a   b   c   d   e

Looking at the boxes from left to right, the number of squares increases by one each time. The new square, added at the end of the pattern, is shaded black; the previous square becomes white. The correct answer is **b**.

Now try these similar questions. Circle the letter under the box that you think is the correct answer.

25. ?

a   b   c   d   e

26. ?

a   b   c   d   e

27. ?

a   b   c   d   e

28. ?

a   b   c   d   e

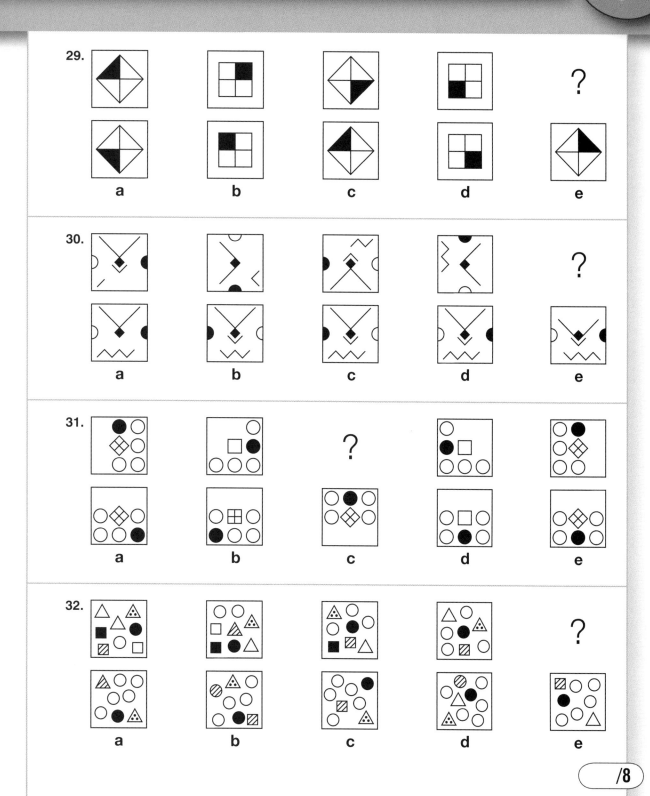

29.

a b c d e

30.

a b c d e

31.

?

a b c d e

32.

?

a b c d e

/8

Example

Work out what makes the two images on the left similar to each other. Then find the image on the right that is *most like* the two images on the left. Circle the letter under the image that you think is the correct answer.

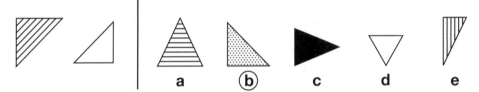

The two images on the left are right-angled triangles with two sides of equal length. Shape **b** is the only other right-angled triangle that has two sides of equal length.

Now try these similar questions. Circle the letter under the image that you think is the correct answer.

33.

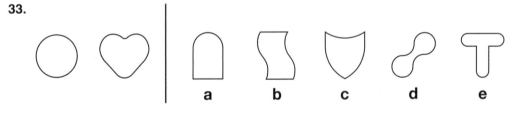

34.

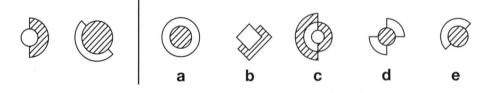

35.

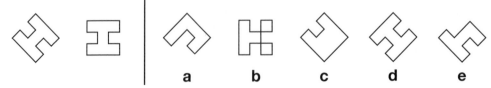

Success
Assessment Papers

More Non-Verbal Reasoning

age 10 – 11

Answer booklet

Answer booklet: More Non-Verbal Reasoning age 10–11

Paper 1
1. d
2. c
3. e
4. a
5. b
6. b
7. c
8. e
9. a
10. d
11. a
12. e
13. d
14. d
15. b
16. e
17. b
18. b
19. c
20. d
21. b
22. a
23. e
24. c
25. c
26. e
27. a
28. e
29. c

30. d
31. b
32. a
33. b
34. a
35. d
36. e
37. d
38. c
39. a
40. b

Paper 2
1. b
2. a
3. e
4. d
5. e
6. c
7. a
8. b
9. b
10. d
11. d
12. c
13. d
14. a
15. e
16. d
17. b

18. c
19. b
20. b
21. e
22. d
23. a
24. d
25. b
26. e
27. d
28. a
29. e
30. d
31. c
32. a
33. e
34. d
35. a
36. c
37. e
38. e
39. b
40. d

Paper 3
1. c
2. c
3. d
4. a
5. b

6. b	**Paper 4**	35. d
7. d	1. e	36. b
8. e	2. e	37. a
9. c	3. c	38. c
10. a	4. d	39. e
11. a	5. d	40. e
12. e	6. d	
13. d	7. b	
14. c	8. b	**Paper 5**
15. b	9. a	1. d
16. e	10. e	2. d
17. e	11. d	3. c
18. c	12. a	4. e
19. d	13. d	5. c
20. e	14. e	6. c
21. c	15. d	7. a
22. d	16. c	8. b
23. b	17. d	9. c
24. e	18. c	10. c
25. b	19. d	11. b
26. a	20. e	12. e
27. e	21. a	13. b
28. a	22. e	14. a
29. c	23. b	15. d
30. d	24. a	16. c
31. e	25. c	17. c
32. a	26. b	18. e
33. d	27. e	19. c
34. e	28. c	20. d
35. d	29. e	21. a
36. d	30. a	22. d
37. e	31. e	23. b
38. a	32. e	24. a
39. c	33. a	25. d
40. b	34. e	26. b

27. b	**3.** b	**22.** b
28. a	**4.** d	**23.** c
29. d	**5.** b	**24.** a
30. d	**6.** e	**25.** c
31. c	**7.** a	**26.** c
32. c	**8.** e	**27.** d
33. d	**9.** b	**28.** e
34. d	**10.** a	**29.** d
35. a	**11.** b	**30.** b
36. b	**12.** e	**31.** d
37. e	**13.** e	**32.** a
38. c	**14.** d	**33.** c
39. e	**15.** b	**34.** c
40. c	**16.** d	**35.** a
	17. d	**36.** b
	18. b	**37.** a
Paper 6	**19.** b	**38.** e
1. e	**20.** c	**39.** d
2. c	**21.** e	**40.** d

36.

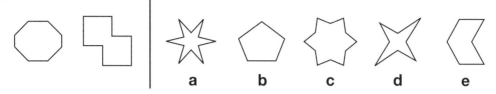

a   b   c   d   e

37.

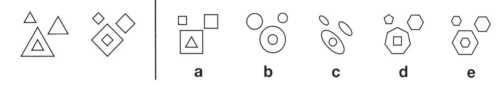

a   b   c   d   e

38.

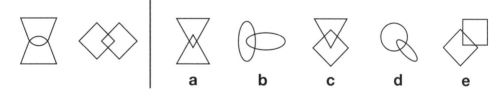

a   b   c   d   e

39.

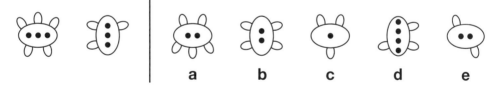

a   b   c   d   e

40.

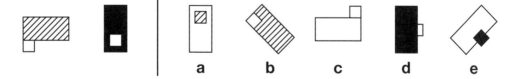

a   b   c   d   e

/8

/40

PAPER 4

Example

One of the boxes is missing from the grid on the left. Work out which of the five boxes on the right completes the grid. Circle the letter under the box that you think is the correct answer.

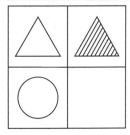

As the images in the boxes move across from left to right, they become shaded with diagonal stripes. The correct answer is **c**.

Now try these similar questions. Circle the letter under the box that you think is the correct answer.

1.

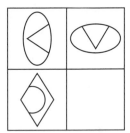

                      a   b   c   d   e

2.

                      a   b   c   d   e

3.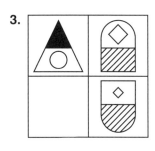

a   b   c   d   e

4.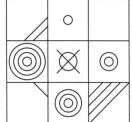

a   b   c   d   e

5.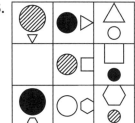

a   b   c   d   e

6.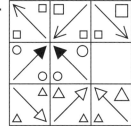

a   b   c   d   e

7.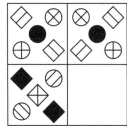

a   b   c   d   e

8.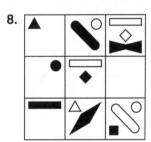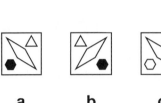

a   b   c   d   e

/8

Example

Look at the line of five images. Work out what connects *four* of the images and makes the other image the odd one out. Circle the letter under the image most *unlike* the others.

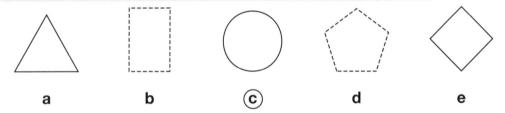

a   b   ⓒ   d   e

Shapes a, b, d and e all have straight sides; shape c is the only curved shape. The shape most unlike the others is **c**.

Now try these similar questions. Circle the letter under the image that you think is the correct answer.

9.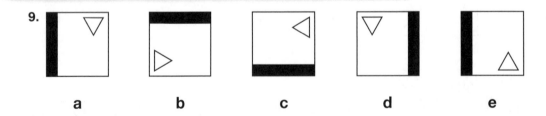

a   b   c   d   e

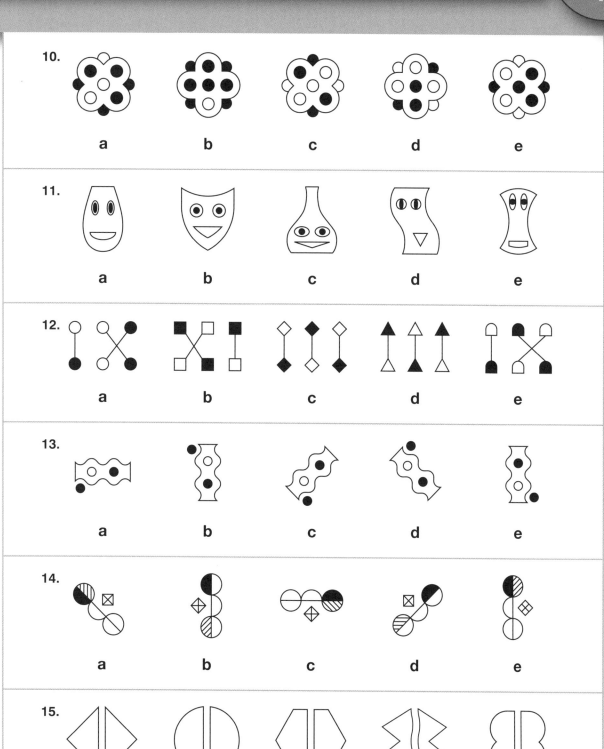

10.

    a   b   c   d   e

11.

    a   b   c   d   e

12.

    a   b   c   d   e

13.

    a   b   c   d   e

14.

    a   b   c   d   e

15.

    a   b   c   d   e

16.

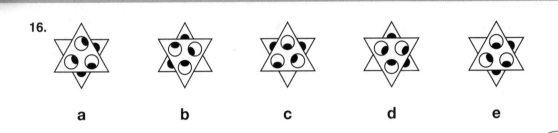

a   b   c   d   e

/8

Example

Work out how the pair of images on the top line go together. Then find the image on the next line that completes the second pair in the same way as the first pair. Circle the letter under the image that you think is the correct answer.

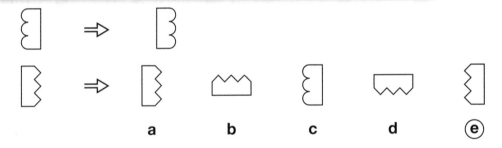

a   b   c   d   e

The images are reflected in a vertical mirror line. The correct answer is **e**.

Now try these similar questions. Circle the letter under the image that you think is the correct answer.

17.

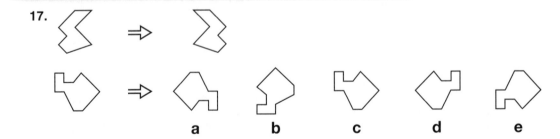

a   b   c   d   e

18.

a   b   c   d   e

19.

a   b   c   d   e

20.

a   b   c   d   e

21.

a   b   c   d   e

22.

a   b   c   d   e

23.

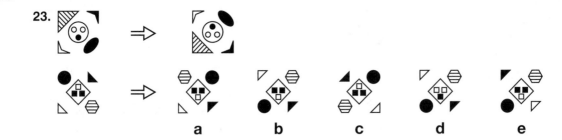

a b c d e

24.

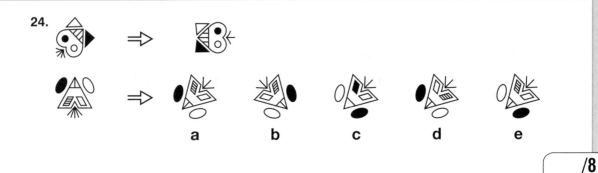

a b c d e

/8

Example

One of the boxes on the second line completes the sequence or pattern on the top line. Circle the letter under the box that you think is the correct answer.

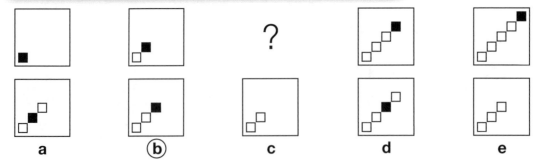

a b c d e

Looking at the boxes from left to right, the number of squares increases by one each time. The new square, added at the end of the pattern, is shaded black; the previous square becomes white. The correct answer is **b**.

Now try these similar questions. Circle the letter under the box that you think is the correct answer.

25.

    ?

a   b   c   d   e

26.

a   b   c   d   e

27.

    ?

a   b   c   d   e

28.

?

a   b   c   d   e

29.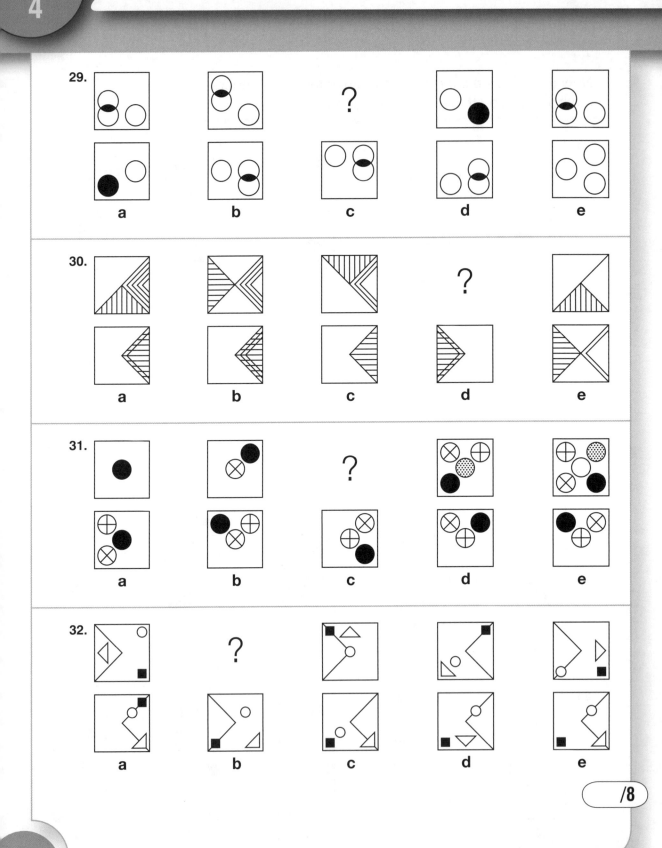

30.

31.

32.

/8

Example

The four images on the top line each have a code. Work out how the codes go with these images, then find the missing code for the image on the next line. Circle the letter under the code that you think is the correct answer.

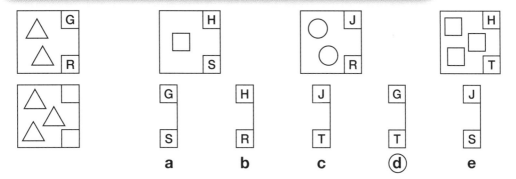

The image with the missing code has three triangles. Triangles have the letter code G. Three has the letter code T. The correct answer is **d**.

Now try these similar questions. Circle the letter under the code that you think is the correct answer.

33.

a

b

c

d

e

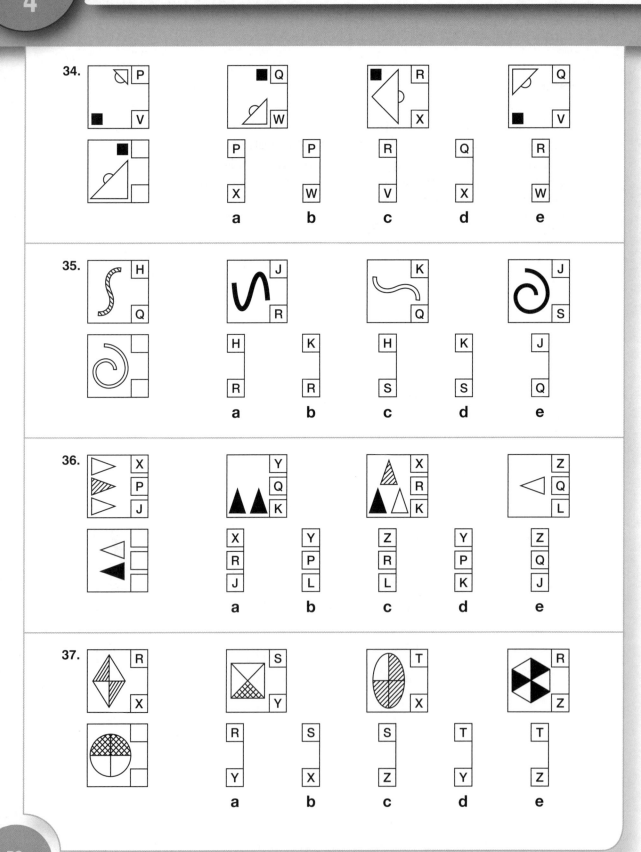

34.

35.

36.

37.

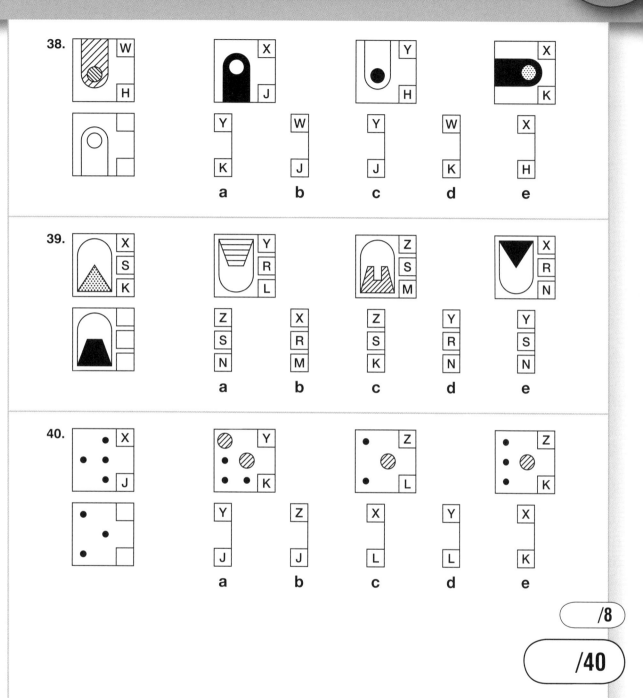

38.

a b c d e

39.

a b c d e

40.

a b c d e

/8

/40

51

PAPER 5

Example

Work out what makes the two images on the left similar to each other. Then find the image on the right that is *most like* the two images on the left. Circle the letter under the image that you think is the correct answer.

 |

            a   (b)   c   d   e

The two images on the left are right-angled triangles with two sides of equal length. Shape **b** is the only other right-angled triangle that has two sides of equal length.

Now try these similar questions. Circle the letter under the image that you think is the correct answer.

1.

  |

          a   b   c   d   e

2.

  |

          a   b   c   d   e

3.

  |

          a   b   c   d   e

4.

a   b   c   d   e

5.

a   b   c   d   e

6.

a   b   c   d   e

7.

a   b   c   d   e

8.

a   b   c   d   e

/8

Example

One of the boxes is missing from the grid on the left. Work out which of the five boxes on the right completes the grid. Circle the letter under the box that you think is the correct answer.

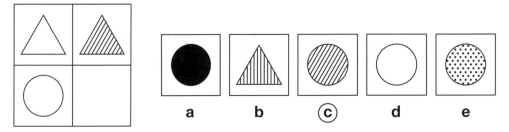

As the images in the boxes move across from left to right, they become shaded with diagonal stripes. The correct answer is **c**.

Now try these similar questions. Circle the letter under the box that you think is the correct answer.

9.

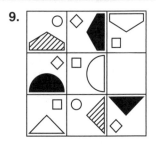

                     a   b   c   d   e

10.

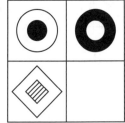

                     a   b   c   d   e

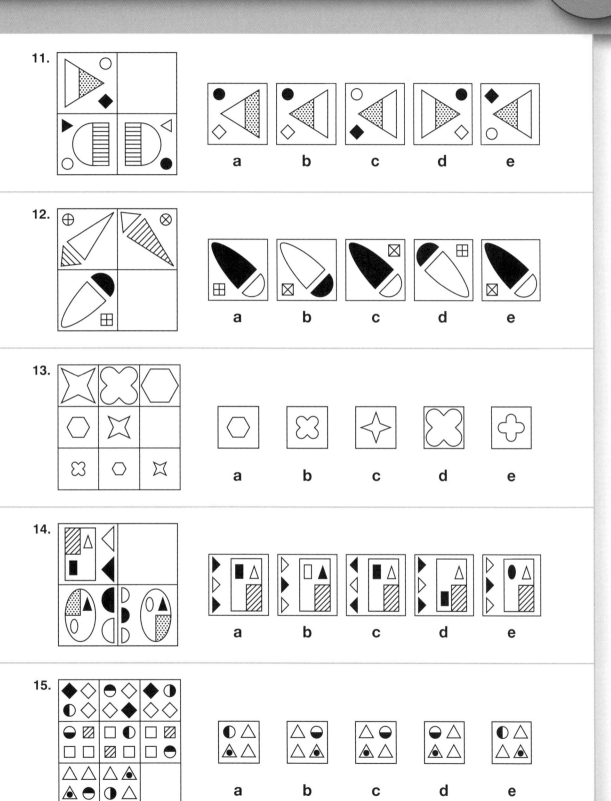

11.

12.

13.

14.

15.

16.

a   b   c   d   e

/8

Example

Work out how the pair of images on the top line go together. Then find the image on the next line that completes the second pair in the same way as the first pair. Circle the letter under the image that you think is the correct answer.

a   b   c   d   e

The images are reflected in a vertical mirror line. The correct answer is **e**.

Now try these similar questions. Circle the letter under the image that you think is the correct answer.

17.

a   b   c   d   e

18.

19.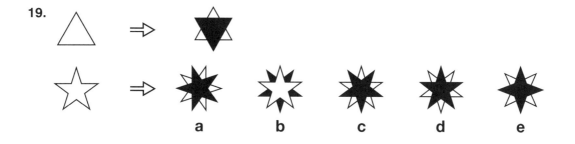

20.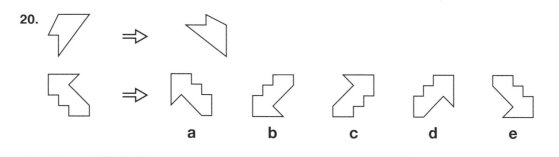

21.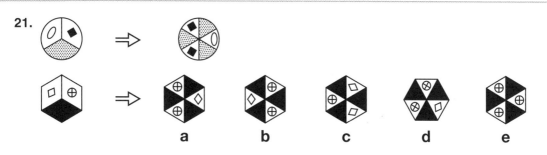

22.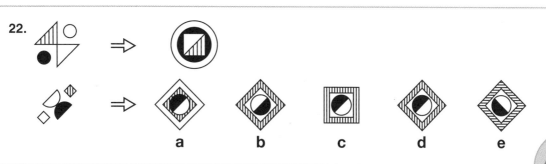

23.

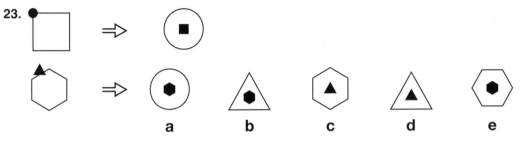

a   b   c   d   e

24.

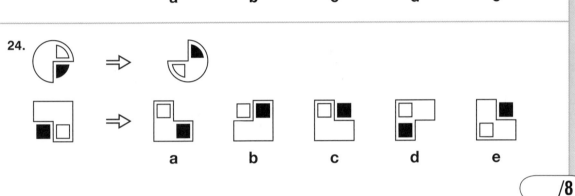

a   b   c   d   e

/8

Example

One of the boxes on the second line completes the sequence or pattern on the top line. Circle the letter under the box that you think is the correct answer.

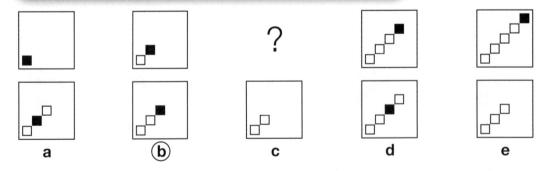

a   (b)   c   d   e

Looking at the boxes from left to right, the number of squares increases by one each time. The new square, added at the end of the pattern, is shaded black; the previous square becomes white. The correct answer is **b**.

Now try these similar questions. Circle the letter under the box that you think is the correct answer.

25.

   a   b   c   d   e

26.

   a   b   c   d   e

27.

   a   b   c   d   e

28.

   a   b   c   d   e

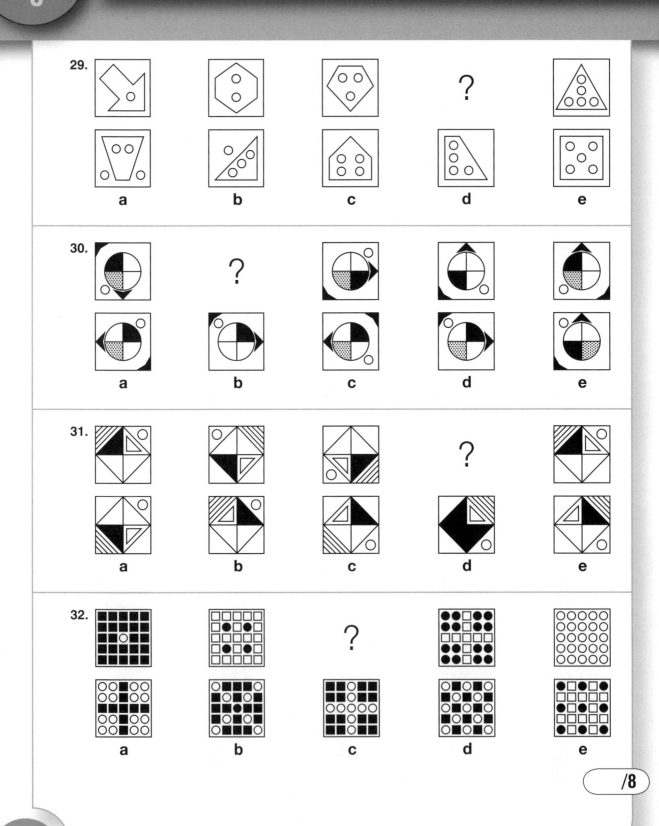

29.

a b c d e

30.

a b c d e

31.

a b c d e

32.

a b c d e

/8

Example

The four images on the top line each have a code. Work out how the codes go with these images, then find the missing code for the image on the next line. Circle the letter under the code that you think is the correct answer.

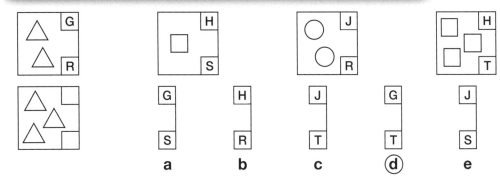

The image with the missing code has three triangles. Triangles have the letter code G. Three has the letter code T. The correct answer is **d**.

Now try these similar questions. Circle the letter under the code that you think is the correct answer.

33.

34.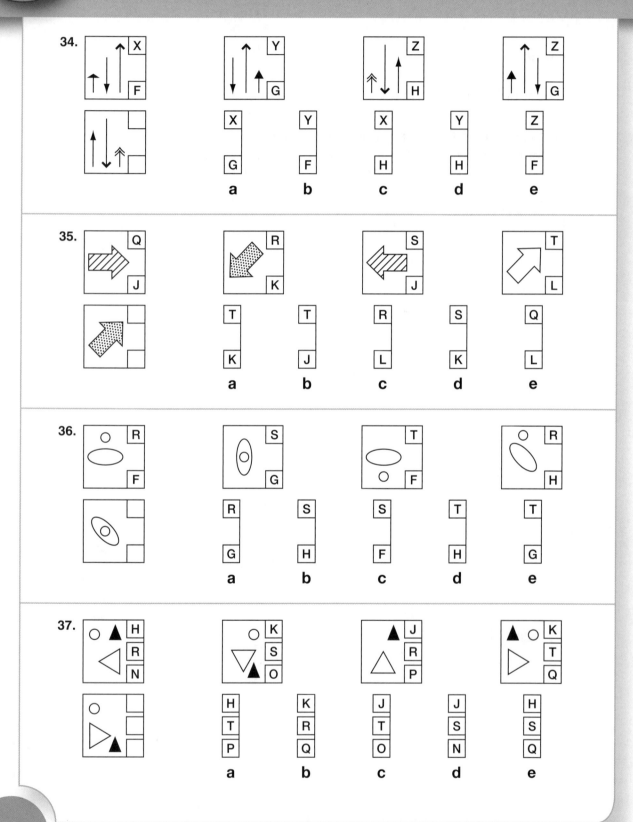

35.

36.

37.

38.

F Q | G R | H S | G T

H R | F S | H T | F T | G S

a   b   c   d   e

39.

P | X Q | Y R | Z Q

Y Q | Z P | X R | Z R | Y P

a   b   c   d   e

40.

K T G | L R G | K R H | M V J

M T G | K R J | M T H | L S H | L V G

a   b   c   d   e

/8

/40

PAPER 6

Example

Work out how the pair of images on the top line go together. Then find the image on the next line that completes the second pair in the same way as the first pair. Circle the letter under the image that you think is the correct answer.

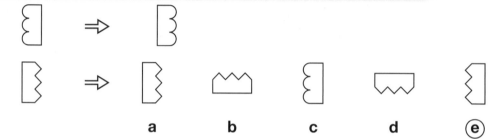

a   b   c   d   e

The images are reflected in a vertical mirror line. The correct answer is **e**.

Now try these similar questions. Circle the letter under the image that you think is the correct answer.

1.

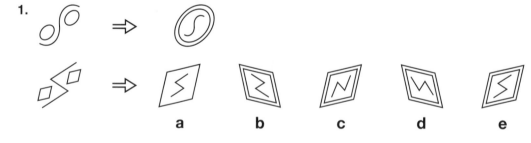

a   b   c   d   e

2.

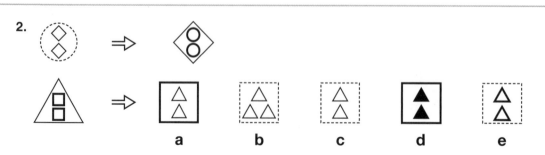

a   b   c   d   e

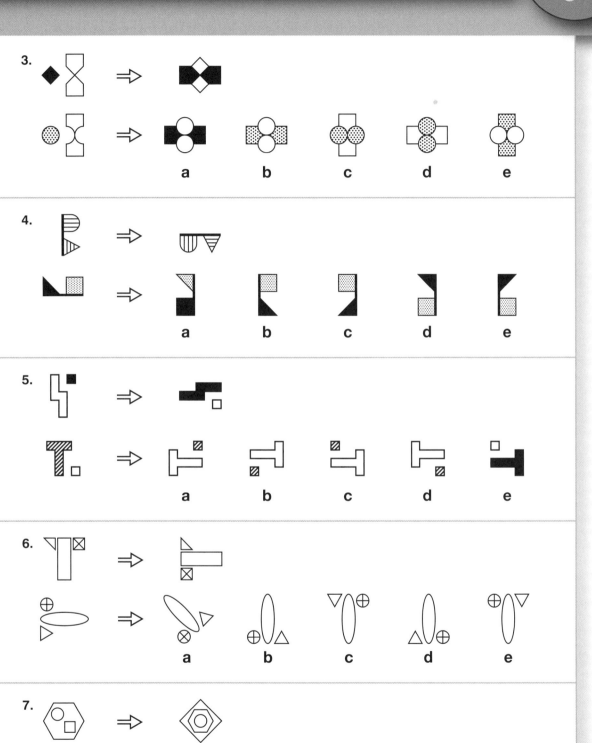

8.

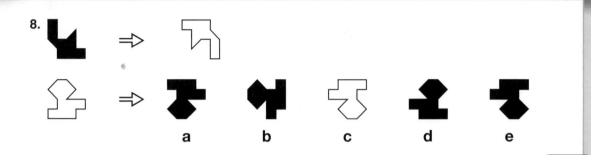

a   b   c   d   e

/8

Example

One of the boxes on the second line completes the sequence or pattern on the top line. Circle the letter under the box that you think is the correct answer.

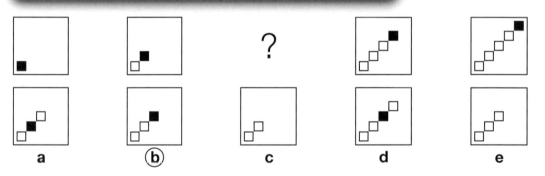

a   (b)   c   d   e

Looking at the boxes from left to right, the number of squares increases by one each time. The new square, added at the end of the pattern, is shaded black; the previous square becomes white. The correct answer is **b**.

Now try these similar questions. Circle the letter under the box that you think is the correct answer.

9.

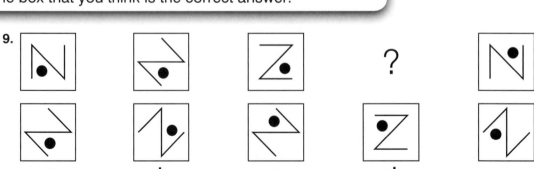

a   b   c   d   e

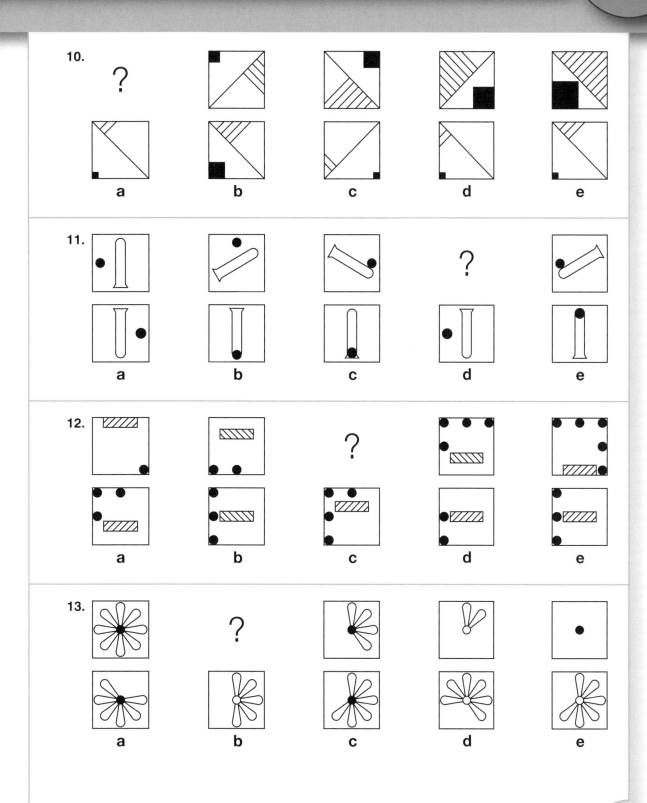

10.

11.

12.

13.

a b c d e

14.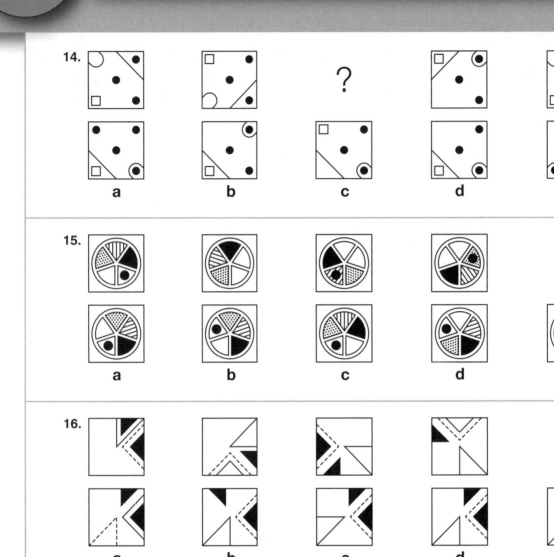

15.

16.

a   b   c   d   e

/8

Example

One of the boxes is missing from the grid on the left. Work out which of the five boxes on the right completes the grid. Circle the letter under the box that you think is the correct answer.

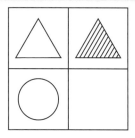 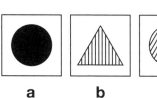

a b ⓒ d e

As the images in the boxes move across from left to right, they become shaded with diagonal stripes. The correct answer is **c**.

Now try these similar questions. Circle the letter under the box that you think is the correct answer.

17.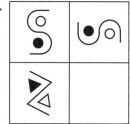

a b c d e

18.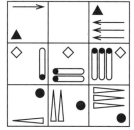

a b c d e

19.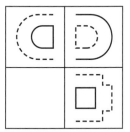

a   b   c   d   e

20.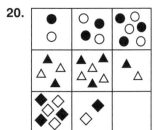

a   b   c   d   e

21.

a   b   c   d   e

22.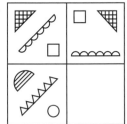

a   b   c   d   e

23.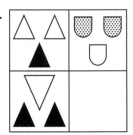

a   b   c   d   e

24.

                               a   b   c   d   e

/8

Example

Look at the line of five images. Work out what connects *four* of the images and makes the other image the odd one out. Circle the letter under the image most *unlike* the others.

    a   b   c   d   e

Shapes a, b, d and e all have straight sides; shape c is the only curved shape. The shape most unlike the others is **c**.

Now try these similar questions. Circle the letter under the image that you think is the correct answer.

25.

       a   b   c   d   e

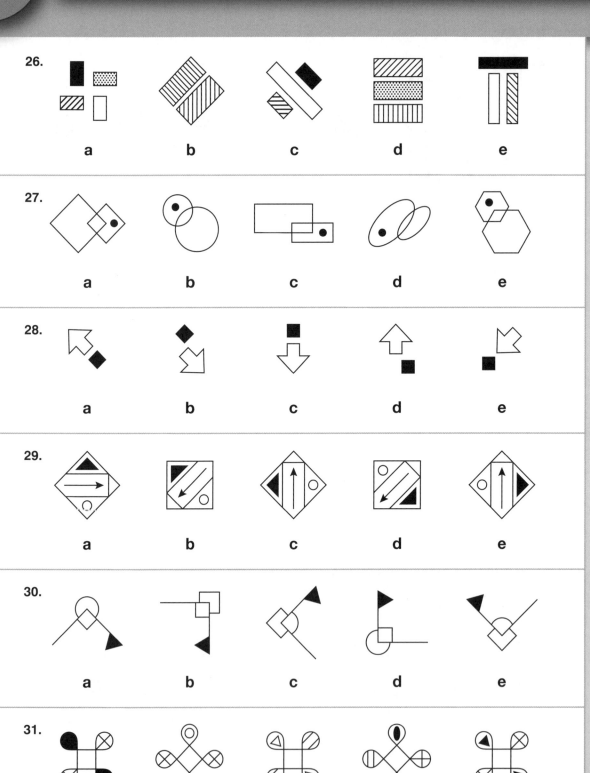

26.

a   b   c   d   e

27.

a   b   c   d   e

28.

a   b   c   d   e

29.

a   b   c   d   e

30.

a   b   c   d   e

31.

a   b   c   d   e

32.

a b c d e

/8

Example

The four images on the top line each have a code. Work out how the codes go with these images, then find the missing code for the image on the next line. Circle the letter under the code that you think is the correct answer.

a b c d e

The image with the missing code has three triangles. Triangles have the letter code G. Three has the letter code T. The correct answer is **d**.

Now try these similar questions. Circle the letter under the code that you think is the correct answer.

33.

a b c d e

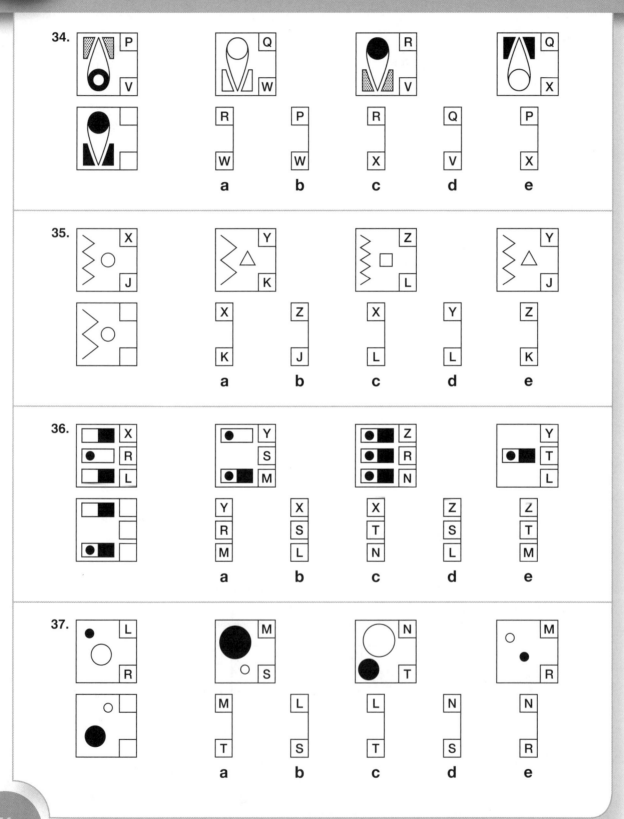

34.

35.

36.

37.

38.

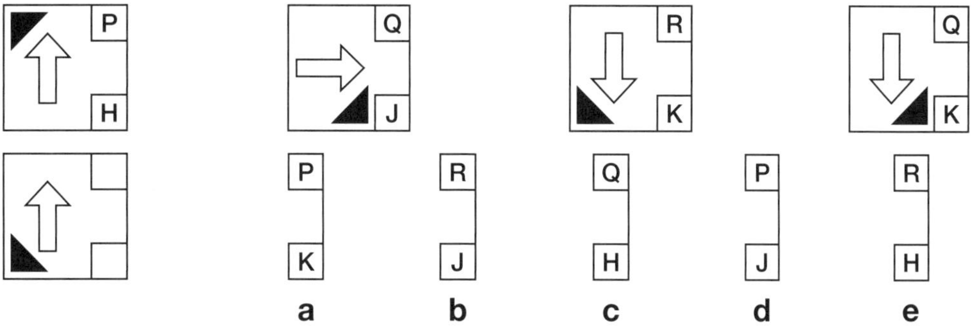

a   b   c   d   e

39.

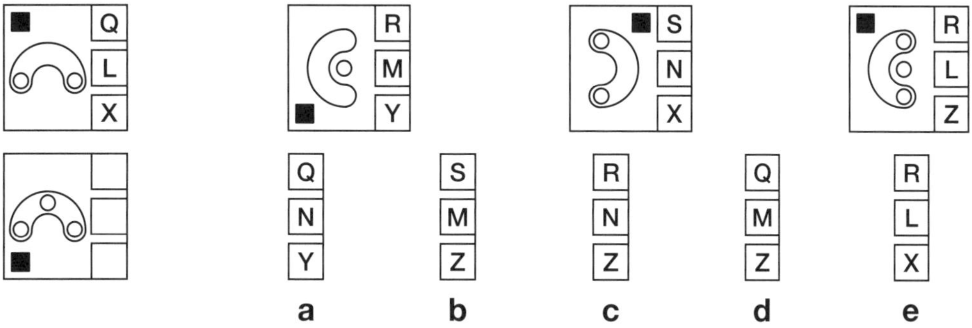

a   b   c   d   e

40.

a   b   c   d   e

/8

/40

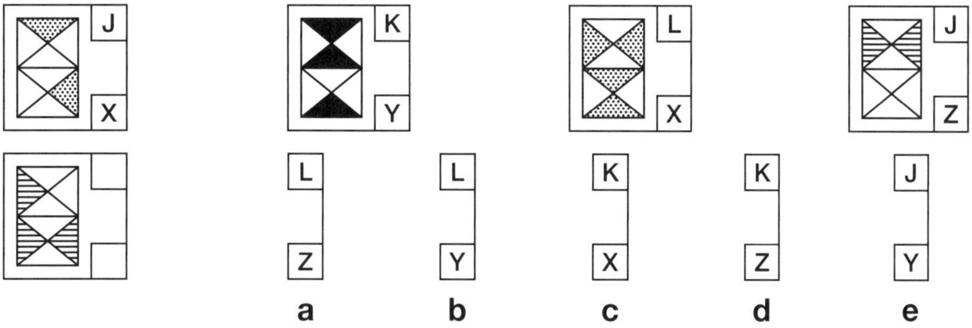

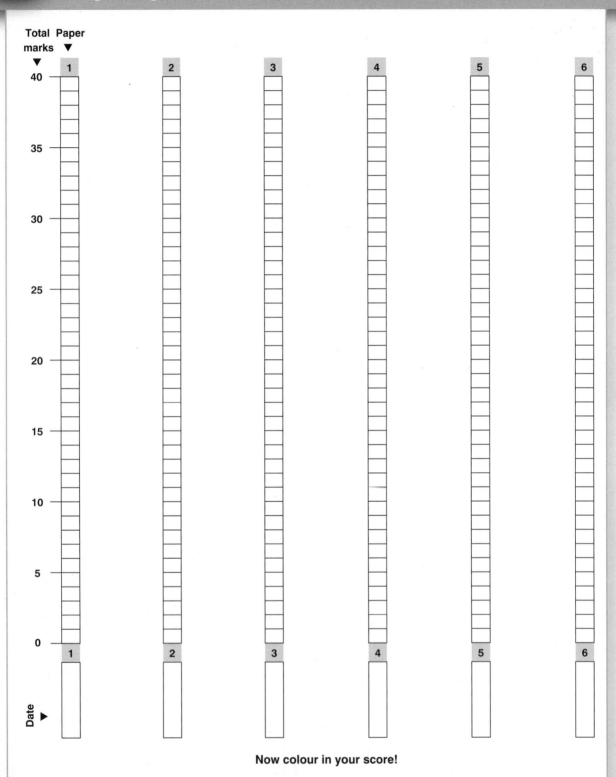

Now colour in your score!